CHRISTMAS SONGS
CREATIVE KEYBOARD

Exclusive Distributors
Music Sales Limited
8/9 Frith Street, London W1V 5TZ, England.
Music Sales Pty Limited,
120 Rothschild Avenue, Rosebery, NSW 2018, Australia.

This book © Copyright 1988 by Wise Publications
UK ISBN 0.7119.1538.5
Order No. AM 71945

Designed by Pearce Marchbank Studio
Compiled by Peter Evans
Arranged by Arthur Johnson
Music processed by A-R Editions Inc.

Music Sales' complete catalogue lists thousands of
titles and is free from your local music shop, or direct from
Music Sales Limited. Please send a cheque or Postal Order for £1.50
for postage to: Music Sales Limited, 8/9 Frith Street, London, W1V 5TZ.

Printed in the United Kingdom by
J.B. Offset Printers (Marks Tey) Limited, Marks Tey.

WISE PUBLICATIONS
LONDON/NEW YORK/SYDNEY

Have Yourself A Merry Little Christmas.

Words & Music by Hugh Martin & Ralph Blane

SUGGESTED REGISTRATION: Electric Piano with Sustain
RHYTHM: Bossanova or Ballad
TEMPO: Slow 96

When the stee-ple bells sound their A, They don't play it in tune

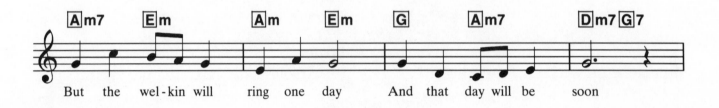

But the wel-kin will ring one day And that day will be soon

Have your-self a mer-ry lit-tle Christ-mas let your heart be light

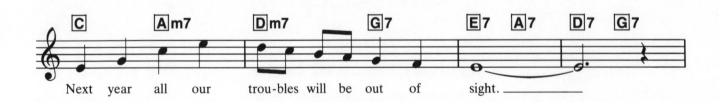

Next year all our trou-bles will be out of sight. _____

Have your-self a mer-ry lit-tle Christ-mas make the Yule-tide gay

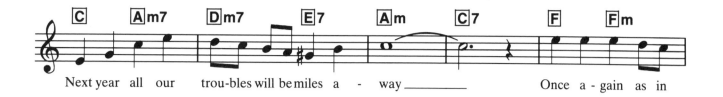

Next year all our trou-bles will be miles a - way _____ Once a - gain as in

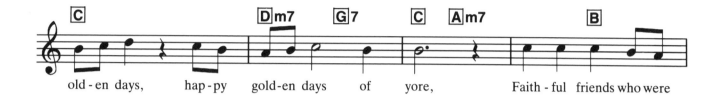

old - en days, hap - py gold-en days of yore, Faith - ful friends who were

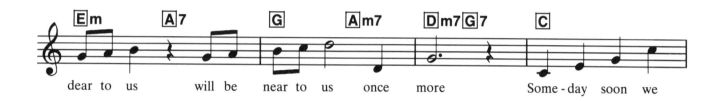

dear to us will be near to us once more Some - day soon we

all will be to - geth - er if the fates al - low Un - til then we'll

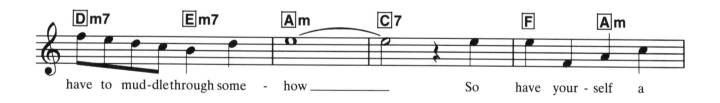

have to mud-dle through some - how _____ So have your - self a

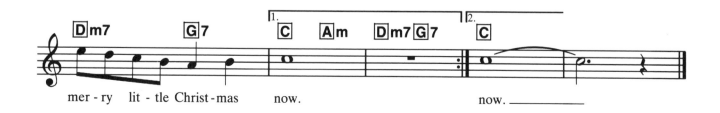

mer - ry lit - tle Christ-mas now. now. _____

Away In A Manger.

Traditional

SUGGESTED REGISTRATION: String or Clarinet
RHYTHM: Waltz (No Drum)
TEMPO: Medium 100

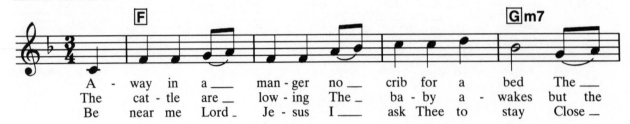

A - way in a ___ man - ger no ___ crib for a bed The ___
The cat - tle are ___ low - ing The ___ ba - by a - wakes but the
Be near me Lord ___ Je - sus I ___ ask Thee to stay Close ___

lit - tle Lord Je - sus laid ___ down His sweet head The
lit - tle Lord Je - sus No ___ cry - ing He makes I
by me for - ev - er And ___ love me I pray Bless

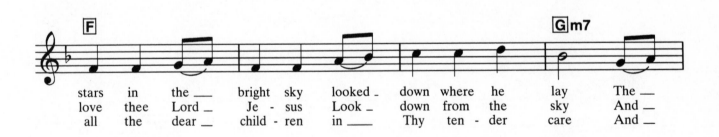

stars in the ___ bright sky looked ___ down where he lay The ___
love thee Lord ___ Je - sus Look ___ down from the sky And ___
all the dear ___ child - ren in ___ Thy ten - der care And ___

lit - tle Lord Je - sus a - sleep on the hay.
stay by my side un - til ___ morn - ing is nigh.
fit us for heav - en to ___ live with Thee there.

4

Sleigh Ride.

Words by Mitchell Parish   Music by Leroy Anderson

SUGGESTED REGISTRATION: Vibraphone with Sustain and Chorus
RHYTHM: Swing or Ballad
TEMPO: Medium 170

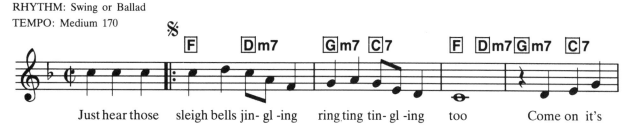

Just hear those sleigh bells jin- gl -ing ring ting tin- gl -ing too Come on it's

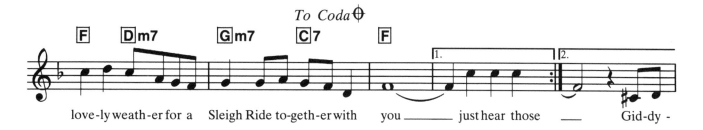

love-ly weath-er for a Sleigh Ride to-geth-er with you ⸺ just hear those ⸺ Gid-dy -

yap Gid-dy-yap Gid-dy - yap let's go let's look at the show we're rid-ing in a

won-der-land of snow ⸺ Gid-dy - yap Gid-dy-yap Gid-dy - yap it's grand just hold-ing your

hand we're glid-ing a - long with a song of a win-ter-y fair - y land Just hear those

you.

Dear Father Christmas.

Words & Music by Lawrette Wright

SUGGESTED REGISTRATION: Vibraphone with Sustain and Chorus
RHYTHM: Swing or Ballad
TEMPO: Medium 160

San - ta Claus gets lots of mail from all the girls and boys.

Ask - ing him to bring them some love - ly Christ - mas toys This

year he had a let - ter that made him scratch his head He's

ne - ver had one like it and this is what it said

Dear Fa - ther Christ - mas we want you to know we

want to make a snow - man but we have - n't an - y snow we

just want a lit - tle e - nough for one day and

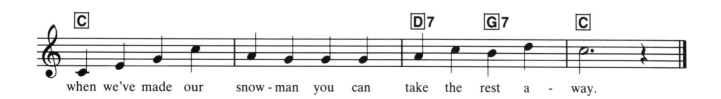

when we've made our snow - man you can take the rest a - way.

Good King Wenceslas.

Traditional

SUGGESTED REGISTRATION: Clarinet or Piano
RHYTHM: Swing or Ballad (No Drum)
TEMPO: Medium 160

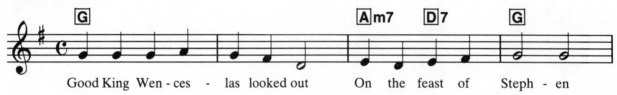

Good King Wen - ces - las looked out   On the feast of Steph - en

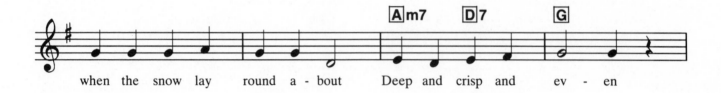

when the snow lay round a - bout   Deep and crisp and ev - en

Bright - ly shone the moon that night   Though the frost was cru - el

When a poor man came in sight   Gath-ring win - ter fu - el.

2. "Hither, page, and stand by me,
If thou know'st it, telling.
Yonder peasant who is he?
Where, and what his dwelling?"
"Sire, he lives a good league hence,
Underneath the mountain;
Right against the forest fence,
By St. Agnes fountain."

3. "Bring me flesh and bring me wine,
Bring me pine logs hither;
Thou and I will see him dine,
When we bear them thither."
Page and monarch forth they went,
Onward both together,
Through the rude winds wild lament,
And the bitter weather.

4. "Sire, the night is darker now
And the wind blows stronger:
Fails my heart, I know not how,
I can go no longer."
"Mark my footsteps, good my page!
Tread thou in them boldly:
Thou shall find the winter's rage
Freeze thy blood less coldly."

5. In his master's steps he trod,
Where the snow lay dinted;
Heat was in the very sod
Which the saint had printed.
Therefore, Christian men, be sure—
Wealth or rank possessing—
Ye, who now will bless the poor,
Shall yourselves find blessing.

Merry Christmas Everybody.

Words & Music by Neville Holder & James Lea

SUGGESTED REGISTRATION: Clarinet or Trombone
RHYTHM: Swing or Dixie
TEMPO: Medium Slow 132

Are you hang-ing up a stock-ing on your wall _____ It's the time that ev-'ry

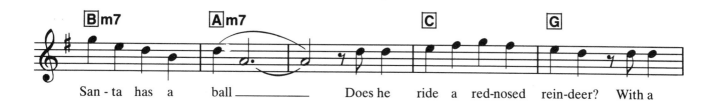

San-ta has a ball _____ Does he ride a red-nosed rein-deer? With a

ton up-on his sleigh _ Do the fair-ies keep him so-ber for a day? _

Chorus

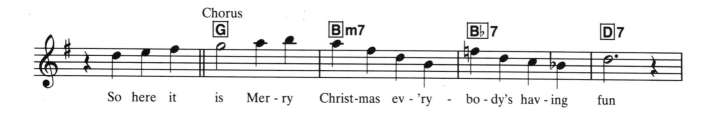

So here it is Mer-ry Christ-mas ev-'ry-bo-dy's hav-ing fun

Look to the fu-ture now it's on-ly just be-gun _____ (Fine)

Interlude

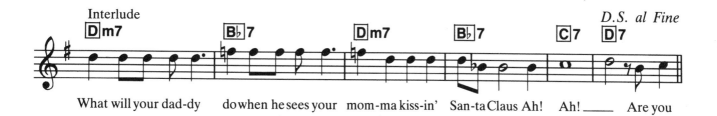

What will your dad-dy do when he sees your mom-ma kiss-in' San-ta Claus Ah! Ah! _____ Are you

Carol Of The Drum.

Words & Music by Katherine K. Davies

SUGGESTED REGISTRATION: Trumpet or Clarinet
RHYTHM: Pop or 8 Beat
TEMPO: Medium 126

Come they told me Pa - rum-pa-pum - pum _____ Our new born

King to see! Pa - rum-pa-pum - pum _____ Our fin - est gifts we'll bring Pa -

rum-pa-pum - pum _____ To lay be - fore the King! Pa - rum-pa-pum-pum

Rum-pa-pum-pum   Rum-pa-pum - pum _____ So to hon - or Him Pa -

rum-pa-pum - pum _____ when _ we come. _____

2. Baby Jesu Parumpapumpum
   I'm a poor boy too Parumpapumpum
   I have no gift to bring Parumpapumpum
   That's fit to give a King Parumpapumpum
   Rumpapumpum Rumpapumpum
   Shall I play for you Parumpapumpum
   On my Drum.

3. Mary nodded parumpapumpum
   Ox and Ass kept time Parumpapumpum
   I played my drum for Him Parumpapumpum
   I played my best for Him Parumpapumpum
   Rumpapumpum Rumpapumpum
   Then He smiled at me Parumpapumpum
   Me and my Drum.

O Come All Ye Faithful.

Traditional

SUGGESTED REGISTRATION: Vibraphone or Pipe Organ
RHYTHM: Bossanova (No Drums)
TEMPO: Medium 112

O come all ye faith-ful Joy-ful and tri - um-phant, O come ye o

come __ ye to Beth - le - hem Come and be - hold Him

Born the King of An - gels O come let us a - dore Him, O come let us a -

dore Him, O come let us a - dore Him __ Christ __ the Lord.

2. See how the shepherds,
   Summoned to his cradle,
   Leaving their flocks, draw nigh to gaze;
   We too will thither
   Bend our joyful foot-steps:

3. Child, for us sinners
   Poor and in the manger,
   Fain we embrace thee, with love and awe;
   Who would not love thee,
   Loving us so dearly?

4. Sing, choirs of Angels,
   Sing in exultation,
   Sing, all ye citizens of heav'n above;
   Glory to God
   In the highest:

5. Yea, Lord, we greet thee,
   Born this happy morning,
   Jesus, to thee be glory given;
   Word of the Father,
   Now in flesh appearing:

A Root'n Toot'n Santa Claus.

Words & Music by Oakley Haldeman & Peter Tinturin

SUGGESTED REGISTRATION: Brass or Piano
RHYTHM: Swing or Dixie
TEMPO: Medium 170

He's a root - 'n toot - 'n San - ta Claus rid - in' rein - deer thru the

sky ____ with his spurs a jin - gle jan - gel - in' __ and his las - so swing - in'

high He's a root - 'n toot - 'n San - ta Claus sad - dle bags all packed with

toys ____ Thru the chim - ney he will bring them all __ to the dream - ing girls and

boys Git a - long lit - tle rein - deer Git a - long_____ cov - er

all the range to - night _____ It's a long long trail _ An

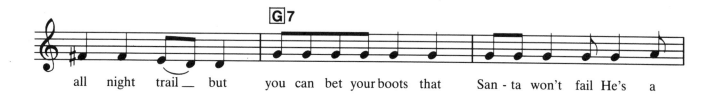

all night trail _ but you can bet your boots that San - ta won't fail He's a

root - 'n toot - 'n San - ta Claus _ And he's on his mer - ry way he will

round up all your Christ-mas dreams _ with a yip-py-yo ki-ya _____ He's a _

It's Gonna Be A Cold Cold Christmas.

Words & Music by Roger Greenaway & Geoff Stephens

SUGGESTED REGISTRATION: Vibraphone or Piano
RHYTHM: Swing
TEMPO: Slow 112

We Three Kings Of Orient Are.

Traditional

SUGGESTED REGISTRATION: Clarinet or Vibraphone
RHYTHM: Waltz
TEMPO: Fast 190

(ALL) We three kings of o - ri - ent are Bear - ing
(MELCHIOR) Born a king on Beth - le - hem plain Gold I

gifts we tra - verse a - far. Field and foun - tain
bring to crown Him a - gain King for - ev - er

moor and moun - tain fol - low - ing yon - der star.
ceas - ing ne - ver ov - er us all to reign.

O_____ star of won - der star of night

Star with roy - al beau - ty bright West - ward lead - ing

still pro - ceed - ing Guide us to thy per - fect light.

3. (CASPER)
Frankincense to offer have I;
Incense owns a Deity nigh:
Prayer and praising, all men raising,
Worship Him, God most high.
  O star of wonder, etc.

4. (BALTHASAR)
Myrrh is mine; its bitter perfume
Breathes a life of gathering gloom;
Sorrowing, sighing, bleeding, dying,
Sealed in the stone-cold tomb.
  O star of wonder, etc.

5. (ALL)
Glorious now, behold Him arise,
King and God and Sacrifice!
Heaven sings alleluya,
Alleluya the earth replies.
  O star of wonder, etc.

15

C-H-R-I-S-T-M-A-S.

Music by Eddy Arnold   Words by Jenny Lou Carson

SUGGESTED REGISTRATION: Clarinet or Jazz Organ
RHYTHM: Swing (2 Beat)
TEMPO: Medium 160

When I was but a young-ster __ Christ-mas meant one thing That

I'd be get-ting lots of toys that day _____ I

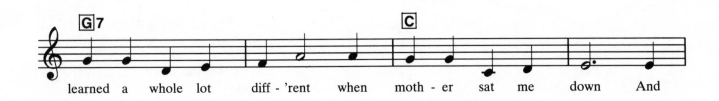

learned a whole lot diff-'rent when moth-er sat me down And

taught me to spell Christ-mas this way _____

"C" is for the Christ child born up-on this day

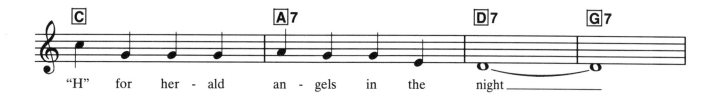

"H" for her - ald an - gels in the night _____

"R" means our Re - deem - er "I" means Is - ra - el

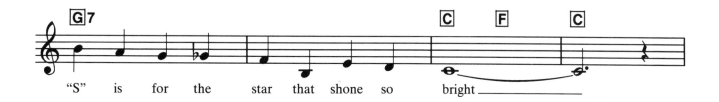

"S" is for the star that shone so bright _____

"T" is for three wise men They who trav - elled far

"M" is for the man - ger where He lay _____

"A" for all he stands for "S" means shep - herds came And

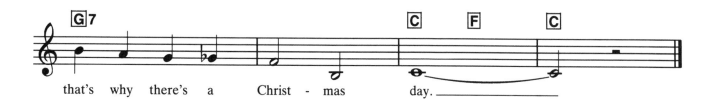

that's why there's a Christ - mas day. _____

Go Tell It On The Mountain.

Traditional

SUGGESTED REGISTRATION: Jazz Organ with Chorus
RHYTHM: 8 Beat or Pop
TEMPO: Medium 120

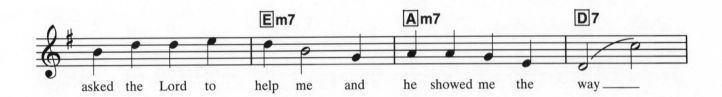

2. While shepherds kept their watching,
O'er wand'ring flock by night;
Behold! From out of heaven,
There shone a holy light.

3. He made me a watchman,
Upon the city wall,
And if I am a Christian
I am the least of all.

4. And lo, when they had seen it,
They all bowed down and prayed;
Then they travelled on together,
To where the babe was laid.

Christmas Candles.

Words & Music by Leo Breen & Wilbur Sampson

SUGGESTED REGISTRATION: Piano with Sustain and Chorus
RHYTHM: Swing
TEMPO: Slow 120

Scarlet Ribbons.

Words by Jack Segal   Music by Evelyn Danzig

SUGGESTED REGISTRATION: Electric Piano with Sustain
RHYTHM: Bossanova
TEMPO: Slow 92

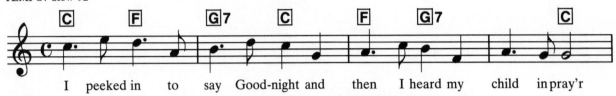

I peeked in to say Good-night and then I heard my child in pray'r

"And for me some Scar - let Rib - bons Scar - let Rib - bons for my hair"

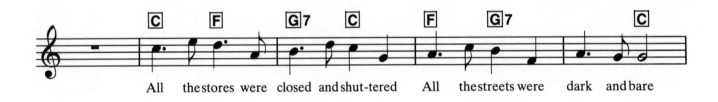

All the stores were closed and shut-tered All the streets were dark and bare

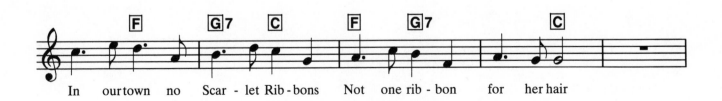

In our town no Scar - let Rib - bons Not one rib - bon for her hair

God Rest You Merry Gentlemen.

Traditional

SUGGESTED REGISTRATION: Vibraphone or Electric Piano
RHYTHM: Swing or Ballad
TEMPO: Medium Fast 180

God rest you mer-ry gen-tle-men let noth-ing you dis - may Re - mem-ber Christ our

Sav - iour was born on Christ-mas day To save poor souls from Sa-tan's power which had

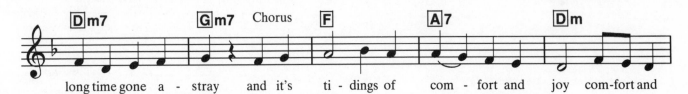

long time gone a - stray and it's ti - dings of com - fort and joy com-fort and

joy And it's ti - dings of com - fort and joy. (D.C.)

2. From God that is our Father.
   The blessed angels came.
   Unto some certain shepherds
   With tidings of the same;
   That there was born in Bethlehem
   The Son of God by name.
   And it's tidings, etc.

3. Go, fear not, said God's Angels,
   Let nothing you affright,
   For there is born in Bethlehem,
   Of a pure Virgin bright,
   One able to advance you,
   And throw down Satan quite.
   And it's tidings, etc.

4. The shepherds at those tidings,
   Rejoiced much in mind,
   And left their flocks a-feeding
   In tempest storms of wind,
   And straight they came to Bethlehem,
   The Son of God to find.
   And it's tidings, etc.

5. Now when they came to Bethlehem,
   Where our sweet Saviour lay,
   They found Him in a manger,
   Where oxen feed on hay,
   The blessed Virgin kneeling down,
   Unto the Lord did pray.
   And it's tidings, etc.

6. With sudden joy and gladness
   The shepherds were beguil'd,
   To see the babe of Israel
   Before His mother mild.
   On them with joy and cheerfulness
   Rejoice each mother's child.
   And it's tidings, etc.

7. Now to the Lord sing praises,
   All you within this place;
   Like we true loving brethren,
   Each other to embrace,
   For the merry time of Christmas
   Is drawing on apace.
   And it's tidings, etc.

Mary's Boy Child.

Words & Music by Jester Hairston

SUGGESTED REGISTRATION: Electric Piano with Chorus and Sustain
RHYTHM: Bossanova or 8 Beat
TEMPO: Slow 94

Long time a - go in Beth - le - hem so the Ho - ly Bi - ble say

Ma - ry's Boy Child Je - sus Christ was born on Christ - mas Day   Hark now how the

an - gels sing a new King born to - day   And man will live for ev - er more Be -

cause of Christ - mas Day   Trum - pets sound and an - gels sing   list - en to what they

say   That man will live for ev - er more, Be - cause of Christ - mas Day.

Winter Wonderland.

Words by Dick Smith   Music by Felix Bernard

SUGGESTED REGISTRATION: Vibraphone or Electric Piano
RHYTHM: Swing or Ballad
TEMPO: Medium 160

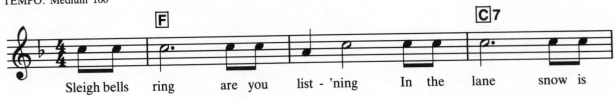

Sleigh bells ring are you list - 'ning In the lane snow is

glist - 'ning A beau - ti - ful sight ___ We're hap - py to - night

walk - in' in a win - ter won - der - land Gone a - way is the

blue - bird Here to stay is a new bird He sings a love song As

we go a - long walk - in' in a win - ter won - der - land ___

In the mea-dow we can build a snow - man Then pre-tend that he is Par - son

Brown ___ He'll say "Are you mar-ried?" We'll say "No man, but

you can do the job when you're in town" La - ter on we'll con -

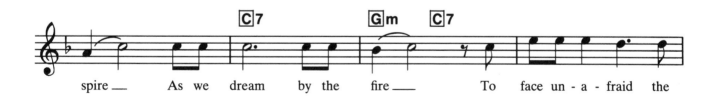

spire ___ As we dream by the fire ___ To face un - a - fraid the

Plans that we made walk - in' in a win - ter won - der - land.

In The Bleak Midwinter.

Traditional

SUGGESTED REGISTRATION: Clarinet or Strings
RHYTHM: Bossanova
TEMPO: Slow 100

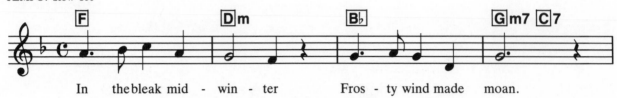

In the bleak mid - win - ter   Fros - ty wind made   moan.

Earth stood hard as   i - ron,   Wa - ter like a   stone

Snow had fal - len   snow on snow   snow __ on __ snow,

In the bleak mid - win - ter   long __ a __ go.

2. Our God, heav'n cannot hold him,
   Nor earth sustain;
   Heav'n and earth shall flee a-way
   When He comes to reign.
   In the bleak mid-winter
   A stable place sufficed,
   The Lord God Almighty Jesus Christ.

3. Enough from him, whom cherubim
   Worship night and day;
   A breastful of milk and mangerful of hay.
   Enough for Him, whom angels fall down before,
   The ox and ass and camel which adore.

4. Angels and archangels
   May have gathered there,
   Cherubim and seraphim thronged the air;
   But only His mother in her maiden bliss
   Worshipped the Beloved with a kiss.

5. What can I give him,
   Poor as I am?
   If I were a shepherd,
   I would bring a lamb;
   If I were a wise man I would do my part;
   Yet what I can I give Him, give my heart.

Walking In The Air
(Theme From 'The Snowman').

Words & Music by Howard Blake

SUGGESTED REGISTRATION: Electric Piano or Vibraphone
RHYTHM: 8 Beat or Pop
TEMPO: Medium 112

We're walk-ing in the air _____ We're float-ing in the moon-lit sky The

peo-ple far be-low are sleep-ing as we fly _____ I'm hold-ing ver-y tight ____

____ I'm ri-ding in the mid-night blue I'm fin-ding I can fly so

high a-bove with you _____ Child-ren gaze o-pen mouthed

ta-ken by sur-prise no-bo-dy down be-low be-

lieves their eyes We're walk-ing in the air _____ We're

danc-ing in the mid-night sky and eve-ry-one who sees us greets us as we fly. _____

Santa Claus Is Comin' To Town.

Words by Haven Gillespie   Music by J Fred Coot

SUGGESTED REGISTRATION: Vibraphone or Clarinet
RHYTHM: Swing or Dixie
TEMPO: Medium 170

I just came back from a love - ly trip a - long the Milk - y Way
Now San - ta is a ___ bus - y man He has no time to play

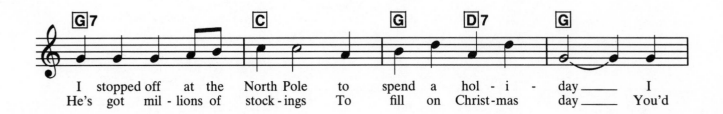

I stopped off at the North Pole to spend a hol - i - day ___ I
He's got mil - lions of stock - ings To fill on Christ - mas day ___ You'd

called on dear old San - ta Claus to see what I could see He
bet - ter write your let - ter now And mail it right a - way Be -

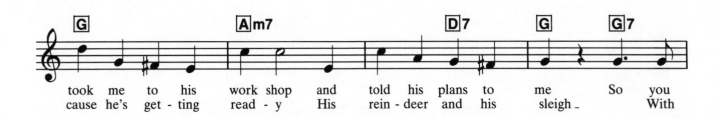

took me to his work shop and told his plans to me So you
cause he's get - ting read - y His rein - deer and his sleigh _ With

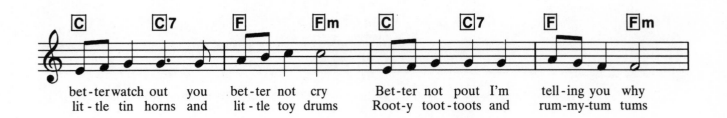

bet - ter watch out you   bet - ter not cry   Bet - ter not pout I'm   tell - ing you why
lit - tle tin horns and   lit - tle toy drums   Root - y toot - toots and   rum - my - tum tums

28

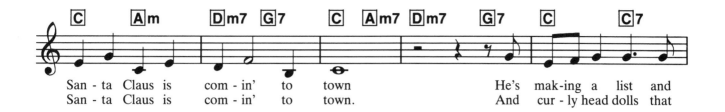

Santa Claus is com-in' to town
Santa Claus is com-in' to town.

He's mak-ing a list and
And cur-ly head dolls that

check-ing it twice
tod-dle and coo,

Gon-na find out who's naught-y and nice
El-e-phants, boats and kid-die cars too.

San-ta Claus is
San-ta Claus is

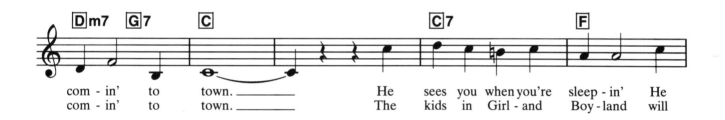

com-in' to town. _____
com-in' to town. _____

He sees you when you're sleep-in' He
The kids in Girl-and Boy-land will

knows when you're a - wake He knows if you've been bad or good so be
have a jub-i - lee They're gon - na build a Toy-land Town all a -

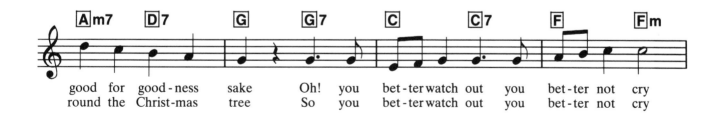

good for good-ness sake
round the Christ-mas tree

Oh! you bet-ter watch out you bet-ter not cry
So you bet-ter watch out you bet-ter not cry

bet-ter not pout I'm tell-ing you why San-ta Claus is com-in' to town.
bet-ter not pout I'm tell-ing you why San-ta Claus is com-in' to town.

D.C.

The First Nowell.

Traditional

SUGGESTED REGISTRATION: Clarinet or Oboe
RHYTHM: Waltz (No Drum)
TEMPO: Slow 96

2. They looked up and saw a star
   Shining in the East, beyond them far,
   And to the earth it gave great light,
   And so it continued both day and night.
   Noel, *etc.*

3. And by the light of that same star,
   Three wise men came from country far;
   To seek for a king was their intent,
   And to follow the star wherever it went.
   Noel, *etc.*

4. This star drew nigh to the north-west,
   Over Bethlehem it took its rest,
   And there it did both stop and stay,
   Right over the place where Jesus lay.
   Noel, *etc.*

5. Then entered in those wise men three,
   Full reverently upon the knee,
   And offered there in His presence
   Their gold, and myrrh, and frankincense.
   Noel, *etc.*

6. Then let us all, with one accord,
   Sing praises to our heavenly Lord,
   Who hath made heaven and earth of nought,
   And with His Blood mankind hath bought.
   Noel, *etc.*

Silent Night.

Words & Music by Joseph Mohr & Franz Gruber

SUGGESTED REGISTRATION: Pipe Organ or Strings
RHYTHM: Waltz
TEMPO: Slow 94

Si - lent night Ho - ly night All is

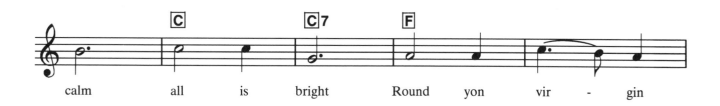

calm all is bright Round yon vir - gin

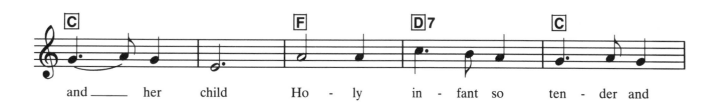

and ____ her child Ho - ly in - fant so ten - der and

mild Sleep in hea - ven - ly peace ____

Sleep ____ in hea - ven - ly peace. ____

2. Silent Night! Holy night!
Shepherds quail at the sight,
Glories stream from heaven afar,
Heav'nly hosts sing Alleluia!
Christ the saviour is born,
Christ the saviour is born.

3. Silent Night! Holy night!
Son of God, Love's pure light;
Radiant beams Thy holy face
With the dawn of saving grace,
Jesus, Lord, at Thy birth,
Jesus, Lord, at Thy birth.

Christmas All Year Round.

Words & Music by Robert Maxwell & Maddy Russell

SUGGESTED REGISTRATION: Vibraphone with Sustain
RHYTHM: 8 Beat or Pop
TEMPO: Slow 114

When the lights are bright up-on the Christ-mas tree And soft white snow is on the

ground Can't help wish-ing it was Christ-mas Christ-mas All Year

Round ____ When there's faith and love on ev-ry smil-ing face, And

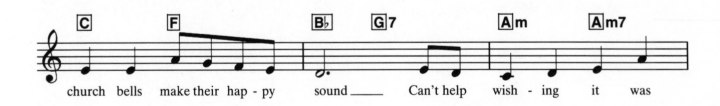

church bells make their hap-py sound ____ Can't help wish-ing it was

Christ-mas Christ-mas All Year Round There's a mag-ic some-thing

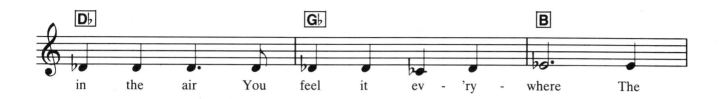

in the air You feel it ev - 'ry - where The

old and gray join the young and gay As they say one sim - ple

prayer _____ "Lord a - bove we pray that we may learn some - day To

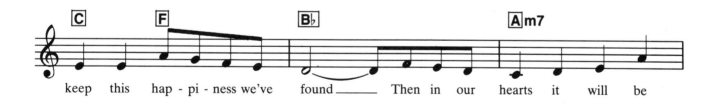

keep this hap - pi - ness we've found _____ Then in our hearts it will be

Christ - mas Christ - mas All Year Round." _____

Ding Dong Merrily On High.

Traditional

SUGGESTED REGISTRATION: Vibraphone or Bell
RHYTHM: Pop (8 Beat)
TEMPO: Medium 140

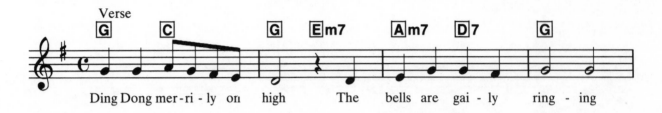

Ding Dong mer-ri-ly on high   The bells are gai-ly ring-ing

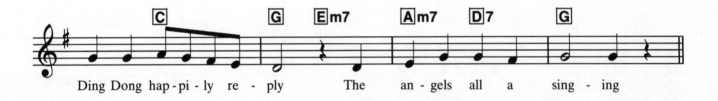

Ding Dong hap-pi-ly re-ply   The an-gels all a sing-ing

Glo - - -

- - ri-a Ho-san-na in ex-cel-sis!

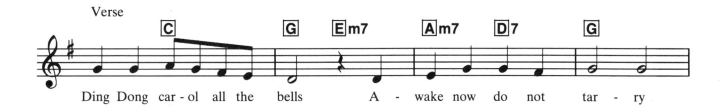

Verse

Ding Dong car-ol all the bells   A - wake now do not tar - ry

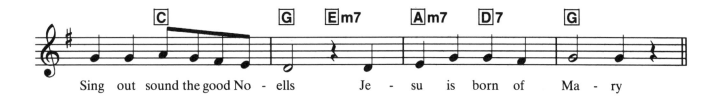

Sing out sound the good No - ells   Je - su is born of Ma - ry

Chorus

Glo - - - - - -

D.C.

- - ri - a Ho - sa - na in ex - cel - sis!

3. Ring out, merry merry bells,
    The angels all are singing.
    Ding dong! Swing the steep bells,
    Sound joyous news we're bringing.
        Gloria, etc.

4. Hark now! happily we sing,
    The angels wish us merry!
    Ding dong! Dancing as we bring
    Good news from Virgin Mary.
        Gloria, etc.

Christmas And You.

Words & Music by Russell Faith & Clarence Way Kehner

SUGGESTED REGISTRATION: Vibraphone or Electric Piano
RHYTHM: Swing or Ballad
TEMPO: Medium 136

I'll re - mem-ber   Christ-mas And   You   All through the

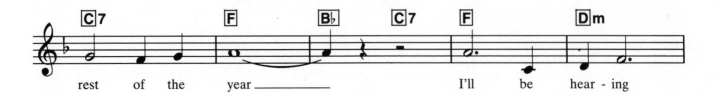

rest   of   the   year _____   I'll   be   hear - ing

jin - gle bells ring   E - ven when spring - time is

near _____   I'll   re - mem - ber ___ our   walk   through the

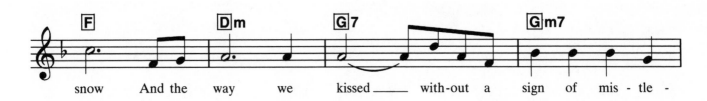

snow   And the   way   we   kissed _____ with-out a   sign of mis - tle -

toe   I'll   be   dream - ing   and   when   I

do,   Christ - mas And   You   will   be   here. _____

Jingle Bells.

Traditional

SUGGESTED REGISTRATION: Vibraphone or Music Box
RHYTHM: Swing or Dixie
TEMPO: Fast 190

We're dash-ing thru the snow In a one-horse o-pen sleigh a-
Bells on Bob-tail ring they are mak-ing spir-its bright what

cross the fields we go we're laugh-ing all the way the
fun it is to

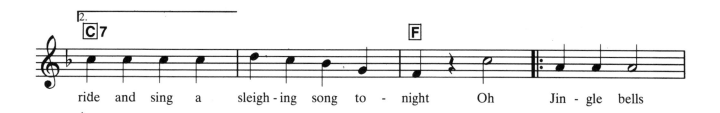

ride and sing a sleigh-ing song to-night Oh Jin-gle bells

Jin-gle bells Jin-gle all the way oh what fun it

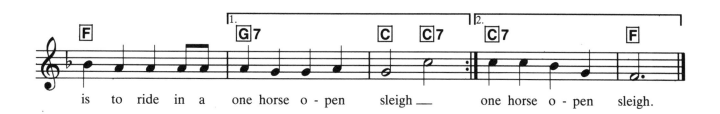

is to ride in a one horse o-pen sleigh ___ one horse o-pen sleigh.

When Santa Got Stuck Up The Chimney.

Words & Music by Jimmy Grafton

SUGGESTED REGISTRATION: Clarinet or Piano
RHYTHM: Slow Rock
TEMPO: Medium 90

When Santa got stuck up the chimney, He began to shout, __ "You

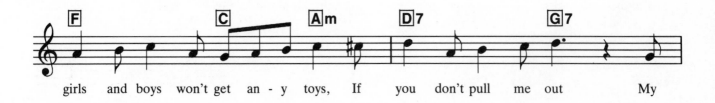

girls and boys won't get any toys, If you don't pull me out   My

beard is black, There's soot in my sack, My nose is tickling too."   When

Santa got stuck up the chimney, A-choo! A-choo! A-choo! __

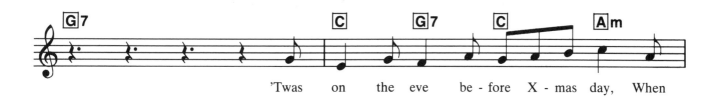

'Twas on the eve be - fore X - mas day, When

San - ta Claus ar - rived on his sleigh, _ In - to a chim-ney he climbed with his sack, But

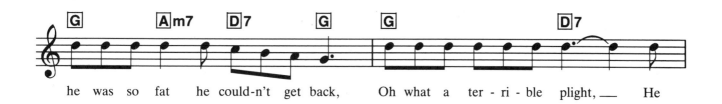

he was so fat he could-n't get back, Oh what a ter - ri - ble plight, __ He

D.S. al Coda

stayed up there all night. When

Coda

choo! A - choo! A - choo! A - choo! *(loud sneeze)*

Frosty The Snowman.

Words & Music by Steve Nelson & Jack Rollins

SUGGESTED REGISTRATION: Clarinet or Electric Piano
RHYTHM: Ballad or Swing
TEMPO: Medium 170

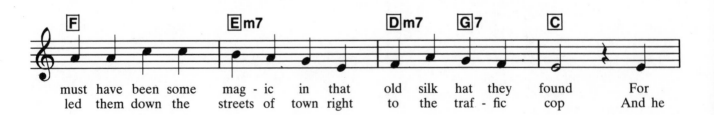

40

Fros - ty the Snow-man was a - live as he could be And the
Fros - ty the Snow-man had to hur - ry on his way but he

chil - dren say he could laugh and play just the same as you and me.
waved good-bye say-ing Don't you cry I'll be back a - gain some day.

While Shepherds Watched Their Flocks By Night.

Traditional

SUGGESTED REGISTRATION: Clarinet or Vibraphone
RHYTHM: Bossanova
TEMPO: Medium 112

While shep-herds watched their flocks by night all seat - ed on the ground The
Fear not said he for might-y dread had seized their troub-led mind Glad

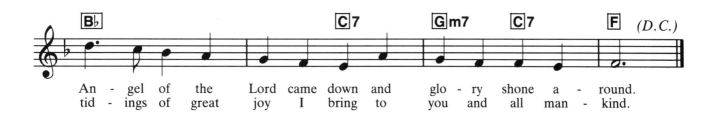

An - gel of the Lord came down and glo - ry shone a - round.
tid - ings of great joy I bring to you and all man - kind.

3. "To you in David's town this day
   Is born of David's line
   A Saviour, who is Christ the Lord;
   And this shall be the sign:

4. "The heavenly Babe you there shall find
   To human view displayed,
   All meanly wrapped in swathing bands
   And in a manger laid!"

5. Thus spake the Seraph; and forthwith
   Appeared a shining throng
   Of Angels praising God, who thus
   Addressed their joyful song:

6. "All glory be to God on high,
   And on the earth be peace;
   Good will henceforth from heaven to men
   Begin and never cease."

The Little Boy That Santa Claus Forgot.

Words & Music by Tommie Connor, Michael Carr & Jimmy Leach

SUGGESTED REGISTRATION: Vibraphone or Clarinet
RHYTHM: 8 Beat or Pop
TEMPO: Slow 86

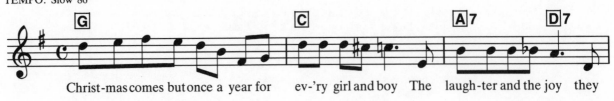

Christ-mas comes but once a year for ev-'ry girl and boy The laugh-ter and the joy they

find in each new toy I'll tell you of a lit-tle boy who lives a-cross the way This

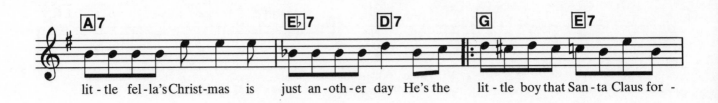

lit-tle fel-la's Christ-mas is just an-oth-er day He's the lit-tle boy that San-ta Claus for -

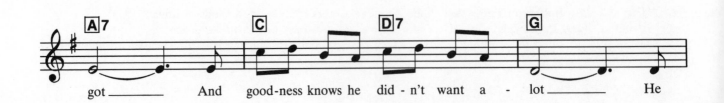

got And good-ness knows he did-n't want a-lot He

sent a note to San - ta for some sol-diers and a drum it broke his lit - tle heart when he found

San - ta had - n't come In the street he en - vies all these luck - y boys _____ Then

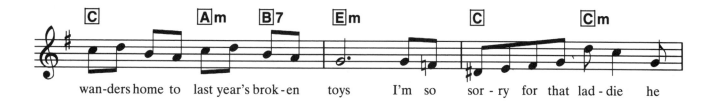

wan-ders home to last year's brok-en toys I'm so sor - ry for that lad - die he

has-n't got a dad-dy The lit - tle boy that San-ta Claus for - got. He's the got.

Deck The Halls.

Traditional

SUGGESTED REGISTRATION: Vibraphone or Music Box
RHYTHM: 8 Beat (Pop)
TEMPO: Fast 126

Deck the halls with boughs of hol-ly   Fa la la la la   la   la la la

Tis   the sea-son   to be jol-ly   Fa la la la la   la   la la la

Don   we now   our   gay ap-par-el   Fa la la   la la la   la la la

Troll   the an-cient   Yule-tide car-ol   Fa la la la la   la   la la la.

2. See the blazing Yule before us,
Fa, la, la, la, la, la, la, la, la.
Strike the harp and join the chorus,
Fa, la, la, la, la, la, la, la, la.
Follow me in merry measure,
Fa, la, la, la, la, la, la, la, la.
While I tell of Yule-tide treasure,
Fa, la, la, la, la, la, la, la, la.

3. Fast away the old year passes,
Fa, la, la, la, la, la, la, la, la.
Hail the new, ye lads and lasses,
Fa, la, la, la, la, la, la, la, la.
Sing we joyous all together,
Fa, la, la, la, la, la, la, la, la.
Heedless of the wind and weather,
Fa, la, la, la, la, la, la, la, la.

Master Chord Chart

	Major	Minor	Seventh	Minor seventh
C				
C# Db				
D				
Eb				
E				
F				
F# Gb				
G				
Ab				
A				
Bb				
B				

The Creative Keyboard songbooks have chord symbols clearly written above the stave. The optional 'seventh' type of chord is shown with the 7 outside the chord frame:

C   C7   Fm   Fm7

The recurring patterns of equally spaced notes (intervals) in Augmented and Diminished chords results in groups of chord symbols having the same note structure:

Augmented Chords

C aug = E aug = G#aug = A♭aug =

C#aug = D♭aug = F aug = A aug =

D aug = F#aug = G♭aug = A#aug = B♭aug =

D#aug = E♭aug = G aug = B aug =

Diminished Chords

C dim = D#dim = E♭dim = F#dim = G♭dim = A dim =

C#dim = D♭dim = E dim = G dim = A#dim = B♭dim =

D dim = F dim = G#dim = A♭dim = B dim =

Keyboard Music Basics

Musical tones are represented by <u>notes</u> written on five horizontal lines called the <u>stave</u>. The position of each note on the stave denotes its <u>pitch</u>.

Notes too high or too low to be placed within the stave appear on short lines below or above it called <u>leger lines</u>.

The specific pitch of notes is indicated by letter-names using the first 7 letters of the alphabet.

A <u>clef</u> sign appearing at the beginning of the staff fixes the pitch or letter-name of one particular note, from which all other notes are related and named in the musical alphabet sequence.

The G Clef (Treble Clef) fixes G on the 2nd line:

The F Clef (Bass Clef) fixes F on the 4th line:

The following illustration shows many of the notes on a keyboard (including sharps and flats) with their letter-names in the bass and treble clefs.

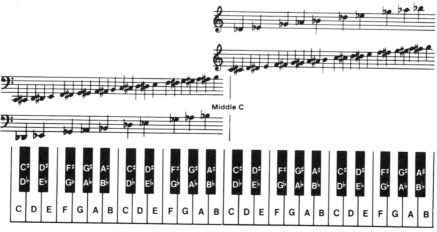

Sharps and flats are placed before notes to raise or lower their pitch by a half-tone (semitone.)
A sharp ♯ raises the note a semitone.   A flat ♭ lowers the note a semitone.   The natural ♮ cancels the
sharp or flat, restoring the note to original pitch.

A key signature at the beginning of each stave indicates which notes are to be played as sharps
or flats, irrespective of their position in or around the stave.   These are the most frequently used
key signatures in the Creative Keyboard songbooks:

C Major A Minor	G Major E Minor	F Major D Minor	D Major B Minor	B♭ Major G Minor	A Major F♯Minor	E♭ Major C Minor

Types of notes with comparative time values are:

Semibreve or Whole Note	=	2 **Minims** or 2 Half Notes
Minim or Half Note	=	2 **Crotchets** or 2 Quarter Notes
Crotchet or Quarter Note	=	2 **Quavers** or 2 8th Notes
Quaver or 8th Note	=	2 **Semiquavers** or 2 16th Notes
Semiquaver or 16th Note	=	2 **Demisemiquavers** or 2 32nd Notes

Eighth notes and notes of shorter duration in time can
be joined together in groups by cross bars called
beams.

1 beam	2 beams	3 beams	4 beams

Music is divided by vertical lines called **Bars** (or bar
lines) into portions called **Measures.**
The total time value in each measure is shown at the
beginning of the music by a time signature consisting
of an upper and lower number. The upper indicates the
number of counts (beats) within each measure; the
lower number explains the time vlaue of each count.

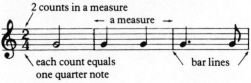

Common time signatures: $\frac{2}{4}$ $\frac{3}{4}$ $\frac{4}{4}$ $\frac{3}{8}$ $\frac{6}{8}$ $\frac{9}{8}$ $\frac{12}{8}$

Special time signatures: C = $\frac{4}{4}$ ₵ = $\frac{2}{2}$ (cut time, called **alla breve.**)

Rests (periods of silence) have time values equal to notes of the same name.

Semibreve Rest	Minim Rest	Crotchet Rest	Quaver Rest	Semiquaver Rest	Demisemiquaver Rest

A double bar shows the end of a composition or
portion of it.

A section of the music to be played twice is indicated
as follows:

repeat the music in between

Sometimes a repeated passage has a different closing
when played the second time. In this instance first and
second endings are used:

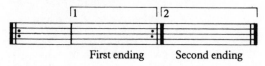

First ending   Second ending

Common musical terms and abbreviations

D.C. (Da Capo) : from the beginning
D.S. (Dal Segno) : from the Sign 𝄋
Coda: meaning 'tail', a separated section of music that forms the end of an arrangement, and is represented by the sign ⊕
D.C. al Coda, and D.S. al Coda : return as indicated and play up to the point marked al Coda, then skip to the Coda section.
Fine : the end.
D.C. al Fine, or D.S. al Fine : return as indicated and play to Fine.

14013 8/92